THINKAT  1

Activities to Encourage Critical and Creative Thinking

Analogies · Language Skills · Categorizing · Brainstorming · Memory Skills · I.Q. Testers

Written by Charlotte S. Jaffe and Barbara Roberts
Cover Design and Text Illustrations by Karen Sigler

ISBN 1-56644-007-6

© 1984 Educational Impressions, Inc., Hawthorne, NJ
Revised Edition: © 1996 Educational Impressions, Inc.

EDUCATIONAL IMPRESSIONS, INC.
Hawthorne, NJ 07507

Printed in the United States of America.

TABLE OF CONTENTS

Teacher Directions and Overview .... page 5

Section I: Analogies .... pages 5-19

Section II: Language Skills .... pages 21-35

Section III: Categorizing .... pages 37-49

Section IV: Brainstorming .... pages 51-63

Section V: Memory Skills .... pages 65-77

Section VI: I.Q. Testers .... pages 79-93

Scoresheet .... page 94

Certificates .... pages 95-96

Overview

Thinkathon activities challenge students' higher-level thinking skills and offer teachers an excellent evaluation tool! This volume is divided into six activity sections: Analogies, Language Skills, Categorizing, Brainstorming, Memory Skills, and I.Q. Testers. Each activity is designed to be completed in fifteen minutes: two for teacher direction and thirteen for student completion. The activities may be used as individual or class practice in these skill areas. They may also be used as an exciting contest!

Directions for Use of *Thinkathon* as a Contest

Thinkathon can be used within one classroom, between classrooms or schools, or among several school districts.

TEAMS
Students are divided into teams of equal number. Each team member is given a creative name tag—flower, animal, book, etc.—which serves as the team name. Students may design their own.

ACTIVITIES
The teams rotate through six activities, each of which is conducted by a group leader. Each activity should be held in a separate area of the classroom or school so that the element of surprise is the same for each team. Each activity page is designed for a fifteen-minute period: two minutes for direction and thirteen minutes for skill involvement; however, the teacher may choose to change the time structure and use more than one activity per contest. Activity pages not used in the contest may be used as practice pages.

SCORING
Each activity section of the book contains directions for scoring. All activities may be done as an individual effort; score one point for each correct answer on *each* team member's activity sheet. Categorizing, Brainstorming, and Memory Skills may also be conducted as a team effort. If a team effort is used, one point is awarded for each *team* answer. In that case the group leader may choose to record the team's answers on the board as the team members call them out and total them at the end of the time limit. A scoring sheet is provided.

CONCLUSION
At the conclusion of the contest, all participants assemble in one location for the awarding of certificates of participation and certificates of special merit (to the winners). These awards may be duplicated from the models in the book.

Section I
Analogies

Suggested Time: 15 minutes
(2 minutes for directions, 13 minutes for skill activity)

This section contains both figural and verbal analogies. Select an activity page of your choice. Although each page is designed to be used in a 13-minute time period, you may decide to use more than one page in the allotted time if your class is more advanced. Briefly review directions for solving analogies. Be sure to stress to your students that they must look for the relationship between the first two items in order to solve the analogy question. When time is up, total the points on each team member's activity page. Each correct answer is awarded one point. Tally each team's total and record it on the Scoresheet next to the team's name.

A-1
Analogies

In order to solve analogy puzzles, you must consider how the first two items relate to one another. Complete the analogies by finding a word that is related to the third word in the same way that the second word is related to the first word. Look at the following example before you begin.

EXAMPLE— Edison : electric light bulb :: Bell : **telephone**

1. palm : hand :: sole : _____?

2. bear : grizzly :: dog : _____?

3. solar : sun :: lunar : _____?

4. calendar : clock :: yardstick : _____?

5. arid : desert :: wet : _____?

6. geometry : math :: cashew : _____?

7. chip : computer :: electron : _____?

8. hurricane : storm :: sedan : _____?

9. army : West Point :: navy : _____?

10. fern : plant :: oak : _____?

11. mouse : mammal :: snake : _____?

12. snapper : turtle :: cobra : _____?

13. U.S.A. : democracy :: England : _____?

14. Antarctica : penguin :: Africa : _____?

15. monarch : butterfly :: mako : _____?

A-2
Analogies

In order to solve analogy puzzles, you must consider how the first two items relate to one another. Complete the analogies by finding a word that is related to the third word in the same way that the second word is related to the first word. Look at the following example before you begin.

EXAMPLE— China : Asia :: Spain : **Europe**

1. three : triangle :: four : _____?

2. river : Mississippi :: ocean : _____?

3. spaghetti : meatballs :: peanut butter : _____?

4. Mars : planet :: toucan : _____?

5. wood : fuel :: meat : _____?

6. fish : school :: seals : _____?

7. ferry : boat :: pick-up : _____?

8. U.S.A. : Stars & Stripes :: England : _____?

9. rosy : pink :: powder : _____?

10. coffee : bean :: tea : _____?

11. tulip : flower :: parrot : _____?

12. beef : steer :: mutton : _____?

14. whale : dolphin :: koala : _____?

15. witch : Halloween :: turkey : _____?

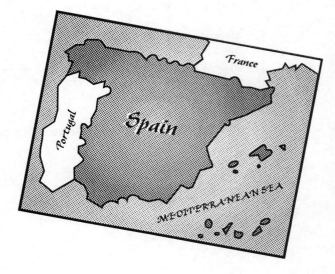

A-3
Analogies

In order to solve analogy puzzles, you must consider how the first two items relate to one another. Complete the analogies by finding a word that is related to the third word in the same way that the second word is related to the first word. Look at the following example before you begin.

EXAMPLE— quart : milk :: dozen : **eggs**

1. May : spring :: October : _____?

2. teepee : Plains Indian :: igloo : _____?

3. stem : plant :: trunk : _____?

4. buffalo : prairie :: squirrel : _____?

5. drapes : windows :: carpets : _____?

6. Washington, D.C. : United States :: Paris : _____?

7. inch : distance :: volt : _____?

8. banana : fruit :: turnip : _____?

9. breakfast : meal :: sandal : _____?

10. skiing : snow :: skating : _____?

11. violin : strings :: piano : _____?

12. stream : river :: bay : _____?

13. Alabama : South :: Vermont : _____?

14. leisure : work :: difficult : _____?

15. hen : rooster :: ewe : _____?

Analogies

In order to solve analogy puzzles, you must consider how the first two items relate to one another. Complete the analogies by finding a word that is related to the third word in the same way that the second word is related to the first word. Look at the following example before you begin.

EXAMPLE— buzz : bees :: laugh : **people**

1. hair : dog :: wool : _____?

2. winner : win :: teacher : _____?

3. hockey : rink :: baseball : _____?

4. drum : beat :: banjo : _____?

5. polite : rude :: smooth : _____?

6. Mississippi River : United States :: Seine River : _____?

7. words : sentence :: musical notes : _____?

8. time : clock :: temperature : _____?

9. tuba : brass :: clarinet : _____?

10. nine : baseball :: five : _____?

11. accountant : numbers :: editor : _____?

12. shout : loud :: whisper : _____?

13. ruler : line :: compass : _____?

14. gluttony: fasting :: culpability : _____?

15. Shakespeare : poet :: Seurat : _____?

Analogies

In order to solve analogy puzzles, you must consider how the first two items relate to one another. Complete the analogies by finding a word that is related to the third word in the same way that the second word is related to the first word. Look at the following example before you begin.

EXAMPLE— cry : sad :: laugh : **happy**

1. dog : bite :: bee : _____?

2. car : garage :: horse : _____?

3. city : state :: state : _____?

4. mail carrier : letters :: schoolbus driver : _____?

5. geologist : rocks :: philatelist : _____?

6. child : boy :: adult : _____?

7. find : lose :: get : _____?

8. dairy : milk :: bakery : _____?

9. monkey : jungle :: dolphin : _____?

10. come : go :: catch : _____?

11. see : eyes :: touch : _____?

12. pupil : class :: player : _____?

13. school : fish :: pack : _____?

14. dog : puppy :: horse : _____?

15. tidy : sloppy :: open : _____?

A-6
Analogies

In order to solve analogy puzzles, you must consider how the first two items relate to one another. Complete the analogies by finding a word that is related to the third word in the same way that the second word is related to the first word. Look at the following example before you begin.

EXAMPLE— paper : pencil :: blackboard : **chalk**

1. sleep : night :: play : _____?

2. child : house :: cow : _____?

3. station : train :: airport : _____?

4. give : take :: back : _____?

5. smart : brilliant :: pretty : _____?

6. ancient : new :: contemporary : _____?

7. nickel : quarter :: penny : _____?

8. reduce : less :: increase : _____?

9. clown : circus :: doctor : _____?

10. city : mayor :: state : _____?

11. 15 : 30 :: 24 _____?

12. tanker : oil :: bus : _____?

13. maximum : minimum :: big : _____?

14. measure : ruler :: weigh : _____?

15. overture : musical show :: prologue : _____?

A-7
Analogies

In order to solve analogy puzzles, you must consider how the first two items relate to one another. Complete the analogies by finding a word that is related to the third word in the same way that the second word is related to the first word. Look at the following example before you begin.

EXAMPLE— candy : sweet :: lemon : **sour**

1. ten : five :: twenty : _____?

2. saw : wood :: hammer : _____?

3. auto : stagecoach :: electric light : _____?

4. hamster : rodent :: koala : _____?

5. amateur : professional :: Little League : _____?

6. help : aid :: tidy : _____?

7. door : molding :: picture : _____?

8. remember : forget :: vanish : _____?

9. Albany: New York :: Helena : _____?

10. hot : oven :: cold : _____?

11. NJ : New Jersey :: ME : _____?

12. indolence : laziness :: zeal : _____?

13. am : were :: now : _____?

14. watermelon : vine :: orange : _____?

15. you : you're :: they : _____?

Analogies

In order to solve analogy puzzles, you must consider how the first two items relate to one another. Complete the analogies by drawing a fourth figure that is related to the third figure in the same way that the second figure is related to the first figure.

1. ⌐ : ∟ :: ⌐ : _____ ?

2. ▬ : ■ :: ❀ : _____ ?

3. D : ○ :: □ : _____ ?

4. ⋙ : ⋘ :: ∿ : _____ ?

5. ○ : ☾ :: □ : _____ ?

6. (cube) : □ :: (capsule) : _____ ?

7. (triangle in circle) : △ :: (circle in triangle) : _____ ?

8. (circle on line) : / :: (heart with arrow) : _____ ?

9. (triangle striped) : (triangle) :: (striped rectangle) : _____ ?

10. (square with N) : Z :: (square with Z) : _____ ?

Analogies

In order to solve analogy puzzles, you must consider how the first two items relate to one another. Complete the analogies by drawing a fourth figure that is related to the third figure in the same way that the second figure is related to the first figure.

1. △ : □ :: ◺ : _____ ?

2. ▦ : ⊕ :: ▭ : _____ ?

3. □ : ○ :: ◹ : _____ ?

4. ◑ : ⊕ :: ◨ : _____ ?

5. ▽ : △ :: ⊓ : _____ ?

6. ◉ : ◉ :: ▣ : _____ ?

7. ⁏ : , :: ? : _____ ?

8. ⌒ : ⌒ :: ⊓ : _____ ?

9. : :: : _____ ?

10. □ : ⊞ :: ○ : _____ ?

A-10
Analogies

In order to solve analogy puzzles, you must consider how the first two items relate to one another. Complete the analogies by drawing a fourth figure that is related to the third figure in the same way that the second figure is related to the first figure.

1. : :: : _____ ?

2. : :: : _____ ?

3. : :: : _____ ?

4. : :: : _____ ?

5. : :: : _____ ?

6. : :: : _____ ?

7. : :: : _____ ?

8. : :: : _____ ?

9. : :: : _____ ?

10. : :: : _____ ?

Analogies

In order to solve analogy puzzles, you must consider how the first two items relate to one another. Complete the analogies by drawing a fourth figure that is related to the third figure in the same way that the second figure is related to the first figure.

1.

2.

3.

4.

5.

6.

7.

8.

9.

10.

Analogies

In order to solve analogy puzzles, you must consider how the first two items relate to one another. Complete the analogies by drawing a fourth figure that is related to the third figure in the same way that the second figure is related to the first figure.

1.

2.

3.

4.

5.

6.

7.

8.

9.

10.

ANSWERS TO ANALOGY SECTION (Some answers may vary. Use your discretion.)

A-1
1. foot	4. ruler	7. atom	10. tree	13. monarchy
2. poodle, etc.	5. jungle	8. car	11. reptile	14. ostrich, etc.
3. moon	6. nut	9. Annapolis	12. snake	15. shark

A-2
1. rectangle	4. bird	7. truck	10. leaf	13. vines
2. Pacific, etc.	5. food	8. Union Jack	11. bird	14. kangaroo
3. jelly	6. herd	9. blue	12. sheep	15. Thanksgiving

A-3
1. fall (autumn)	4. forest	7. electricity	10. ice	13. New England
2. Eskimo	5. floors	8. vegetable	11. keys	14. easy
3. tree	6. France	9. shoe	12. ocean	15. ram

A-4
1. sheep	4. strum	7. melody	10. basketball	13. circle
2. teach	5. rough	8. thermometer	11. words	14. innocence
3. field	6. France	9. wood	12. soft	15. painter (artist)

A-5
1. sting	4. students	7. give	10. throw	13. wolves
2. stable	5. stamps	8. bread	11. hands	14. colt
3. nation	6. man	9. sea	12. team	15. shut (closed)

A-6
1. day	4. front	7. nickel	10. governor	13. little
2. barn	5. beautiful	8. more	11. 48	14. scale
3. plane	6. old	9. hospital	12. people	15. book (speech)

A-7
1. ten	4. marsupial	7. frame	10. refrigerator	13. before
2. nail	5. Major League	8. appear	11. Maine	14. tree
3. candle	6. neat	9. Montana	12. enthusiasm	15. they're

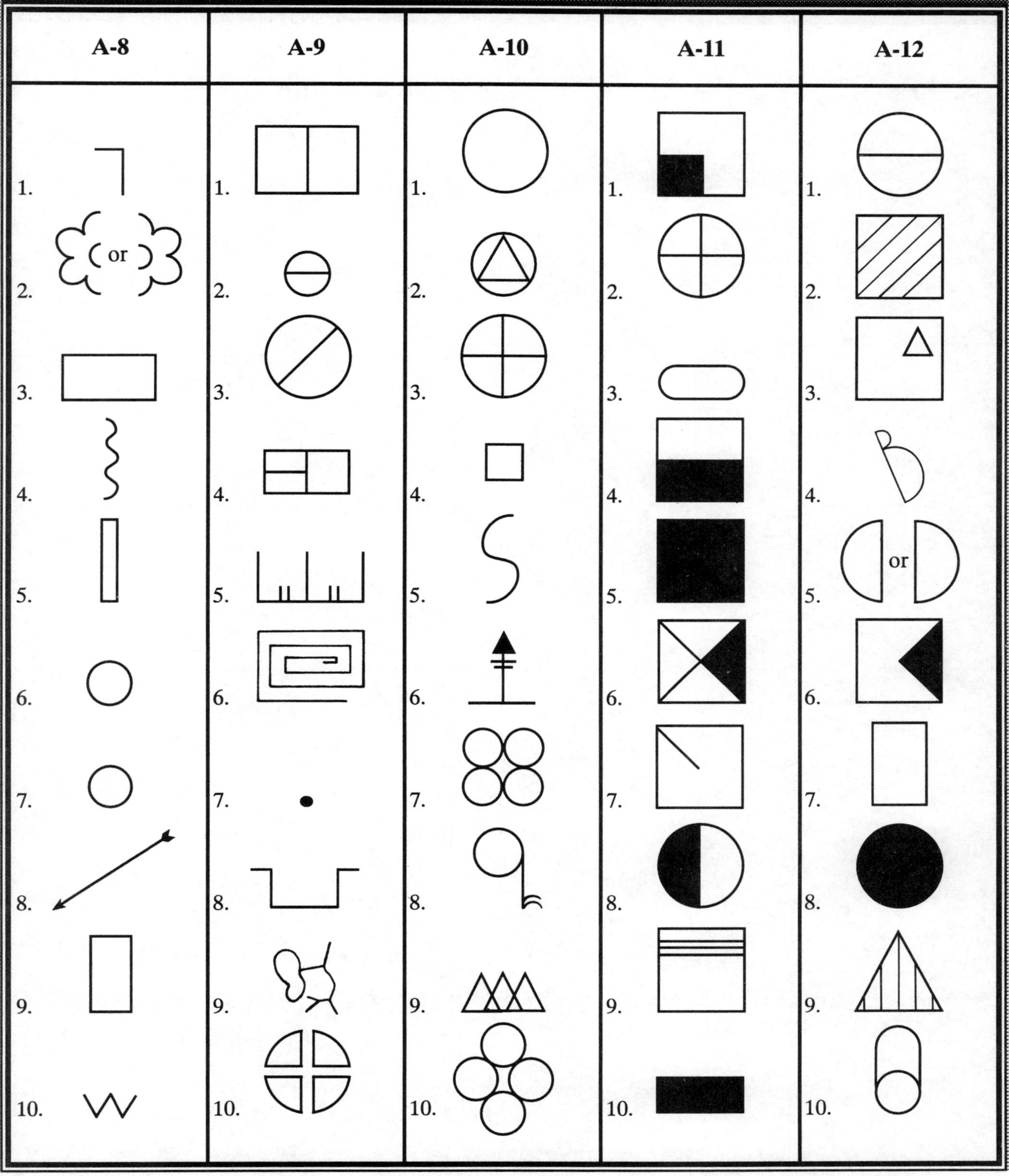
A-8
A-9
A-10
A-11
A-12
1.
2.
or
3.
4.
5.
or
6.
7.
8.
9.
10.

Section II
Language Skills

Suggested Time: 15 minutes

(2 minutes for directions, 13 minutes for skill activity)

The activities in this section contain a variety of word arrangements. Students must supply a missing word for each set on the page. Although each page is designed to be used in a 13-minute time period, you may decide to use more than one page in the allotted time if your class is more advanced. When time is up, total the points on each team member's activity page. Each correct answer is awarded one point. Tally each team's total and record it on the Scoresheet next to the team's name.

Language Skills: What Comes Before?

Complete the familiar expressions, phrases, or compounds by adding the same word to each blank in the set. Look at the following example before you begin.

EXAMPLE: _____rise _____shine _____spot

Answer: sun

1. _____cream _____cube _____water
2. _____sick _____break _____felt
3. _____hand _____yard _____door
4. _____style _____saver _____span
5. _____house _____food _____days
6. _____bridge _____string _____knife
7. _____foot _____ware _____worm
8. _____back _____deck _____final _____master
9. _____gone _____close _____cast _____father
10. _____lord _____slide _____lubber _____mark
11. _____paper _____room _____stand _____reel
12. _____block _____runner _____side _____work
13. _____dust _____horse _____mill _____toothed
14. _____yard _____mate _____shape _____wreck
15. _____ball _____boiled _____hearted _____knocks

Language Skills: What Comes Before?

Complete the familiar expressions, phrases, or compounds by adding the same word to each blank in the set. Look at the following example before you begin.

EXAMPLE: _____cut _____brush _____style
Answer: hair

1. _____bug _____rest _____spread

2. _____stand _____shake _____held

3. _____seat _____bird _____sick

4. _____horse _____shell _____shore

5. _____some _____bag _____shake

6. _____ground _____mate _____thing

7. _____back _____weight _____doll

8. _____ball _____rest _____light _____print

9. _____boat _____keeper _____hold _____fly

10. _____bow _____coat _____drop _____spout

11. _____cheese _____fish _____streak _____jay

12. _____word _____book _____port _____out

13. _____slam _____parent _____stand _____child

14. _____shoes _____flake _____ball _____man

15. _____wind _____walk _____word _____stitch

Language Skills: What Comes Before?

Complete the familiar expressions, phrases, or compounds by adding the same word to each blank in the set. Look at the following example before you begin.

EXAMPLE: _____shave _____call _____quarters
Answer: close

1. _____rib _____Minister _____meridian

2. _____touch _____spoken _____soap

3. _____pox _____coop _____salad

4. _____cheese _____chocolate _____watches

5. _____market _____ball _____hole

6. _____fry _____toast _____perfume

7. _____word _____over _____country

8. _____Sea _____carpet _____hot _____cent

9. _____brain _____watching _____bath _____house

10. _____hunter _____wind _____light _____stand

11. _____box _____pane _____dressing _____shopping

12. _____closet _____town _____cabinet _____doll

13. _____frame _____window _____perfect _____book

14. _____man _____crack _____up _____guy

15. _____white _____beater _____roll _____head

Language Skills: What Comes Before?

Complete the familiar expressions, phrases, or compounds by adding the same word to each blank in the set. Look at the following example before you begin.

EXAMPLE: _____ light _____ shine _____ flower

Answer: sun

1. _____ bowl _____ bar _____ dressing

2. _____ bill _____ company _____ heater

3. _____ cash _____ front _____ heart

4. _____ blood _____ grass _____ moon

5. _____ keg _____ puff _____ blue

6. _____ shaker _____ mine _____ water

7. _____ springs _____ water _____ oil

8. _____ bell _____ chip _____ ribbon _____ cheese

9. _____ step _____ show _____ yard _____ walk

10. _____ lily _____ basket _____ bonnet _____ parade

11. _____ crab _____ castle _____ dune _____ dollar

12. _____ worm _____ flowers _____ stockings _____ suit

13. _____ switch _____ duty _____ house _____ weight

14. _____ band _____ tower _____ man _____ out

15. _____ apple _____ grass _____ cake _____ shell

Language Skills: What Comes After?

Complete the familiar expressions, phrases, or compounds by adding the same word to each blank in the set. Look at the following example before you begin.

EXAMPLE: chest_____   dough_____   pea_____
Answer: nut

1. nut_____   clam_____   egg_____

2. broad_____   fore_____   out_____

3. rest_____   use_____   hope_____

4. hand_____   sand_____   tote_____

5. stead_____   break_____   stand_____

6. thunder_____   snow_____   ice_____

7. flood_____   star_____   electric_____

8. net_____   clock_____   home_____   road_____

9. scholar_____   friend_____   hard_____   leader_____

10. stair_____   suit_____   brief_____   show_____

11. score_____   sea_____   skate_____   chalk_____

12. draw_____   quarter_____   hump_____   feed_____

13. straw_____   blue_____   black_____   goose_____

14. country_____   bed_____   out_____   fire_____

15. laser_____   sun_____   wooden_____   light_____

Language Skills: What Comes After?

Complete the familiar expressions, phrases, or compounds by adding the same word to each blank in the set. Look at the following example before you begin.

EXAMPLE: over_____   chalk_____   bulletin_____
Answer: board

1. pound_____   fruit_____   short_____

2. head_____   one_____   walk_____

3. thumb_____   roofing_____   finishing_____

4. grape_____   dried_____   Kiwi_____

5. loose_____   maple_____   table_____

6. stained_____   plate_____   cut_____

7. bread_____   walking_____   peppermint_____

8. back_____   head_____   bread_____   cutting_____

9. desk_____   table_____   box_____   black_____

10. micro_____   tidal_____   radio_____   short_____

11. cereal_____   fuse_____   cash_____   ice_____

12. fly_____   tissue_____   writing_____   wall_____

13. view_____   pencil_____   ball_____   pin_____

14. tree_____   fire_____   hen_____   dog_____

15. clothes_____   shoe_____   family_____   fir_____

Language Skills: What Comes After?

Complete the familiar expressions, phrases, or compounds by adding the same word to each blank in the set. Look at the following example before you begin.

EXAMPLE: head_____   corner_____   Yellow_____
Answer: stone

1. overdue_____   dollar_____   electric_____

2. navy_____   true_____   powder_____

3. water_____   oil_____   finger_____

4. hard_____   glass_____   silver_____

5. paper_____   saw_____   sugar_____

6. butcher_____   cement_____   cinder_____

7. lime_____   sand_____   gem_____

8. apple_____   lime_____   kelly_____   olive_____

9. out_____   yard_____   base_____   clothes_____

10. salad_____   sand_____   handle_____   candy_____

11. screen_____   storm_____   Dutch_____   open_____

12. beet_____   apple_____   blood_____   bright_____

13. dead_____   private_____   black_____   bull's_____

14. soy_____   wax_____   green_____   string_____

15. even_____   safety_____   tennis_____   boxing_____

Language Skills: What Comes After?

Complete the familiar expressions, phrases, or compounds by adding the same word to each blank in the set. Look at the following example before you begin.

EXAMPLE: candle_____   yard_____   match_____
Answer: stick

1. jet_____   pitch_____   in the_____

2. sweet_____   chick_____   green_____

3. silver_____   measuring_____   serving_____

4. whole_____   hand_____   lone_____

5. wagon_____   spinning_____   big_____

6. dill_____   milk_____   butterfly_____

7. butter_____   ice_____   skim_____

8. white_____   ski_____   snow_____   baseball_____

9. lady_____   June_____   stink_____   pill_____

10. dragon_____   house_____   butter_____   horse_____

11. egg_____   crab_____   turtle_____   nut_____

12. meat_____   sour_____   gum_____   butter_____

13. table_____   chair_____   wooden_____   peg_____

14. back_____   helping_____   fore_____   short_____

15. note_____   phone_____   over_____   library_____

Language Skills:
What Comes Before or After?

Complete the familiar expressions, phrases, or compounds by adding the same word to each blank in the set. Look at the following example before you begin.

EXAMPLE: saw_____   _____play   _____back
Answer: horse

1. Mother_____   _____mover   _____worm

2. _____corn   soda_____   _____over

3. _____pie   flower_____   coffee_____

4. _____guest   doll_____   _____call

5. whole_____   _____where   _____thing

6. _____front   white_____   _____proof

7. silly_____   _____down   _____berry

8. _____walk   road_____   out_____   _____winder

9. out_____   _____man   _____way   storm_____

10. ticket_____   straight_____   hard_____   _____up

11. _____drain   _____door   snow_____   _____warning

12. _____pod   _____nut   sweet_____   _____hen

13. grape_____   _____juice   candied_____   _____tree

14. water_____   _____being   wishing_____   get_____

15. fish_____   safety_____   hair_____   _____work

Language Skills:
What Comes Before or After?

Complete the familiar expressions, phrases, or compounds by adding the same word to each blank in the set. Look at the following example before you begin.

EXAMPLE: friend_____   _____wreck   _____shape
Answer: ship

1. more_____   _____coat   _____see

2. _____mill   see_____   chain_____

3. _____bird   _____top   pitch_____

4. fire_____   some_____   _____mat

5. law_____   sweat_____   bathing_____

6. first_____   _____mate   _____room

7. _____court   table_____   _____match

8. lumber_____   _____stick   _____work   _____goods

9. black_____   butter_____   _____game   _____joint

10. yard_____   cinnamon_____   _____pin   _____up

11. _____green   _____glade   where_____   how_____

12. hot_____   _____boat   green_____   _____plant

13. _____bag   _____leaf   iced_____   _____pot

14. heart_____   _____fast   _____out   _____able

15. clock_____   _____man   home_____   _____book

Language Skills:
What Comes Before or After?

Complete the familiar expressions, phrases, or compounds by adding the same word to each blank in the set. Look at the following example before you begin.

EXAMPLE: play_____   _____salad   _____wing
Answer: chicken

1. _____stakes   chimney_____   clean_____

2. air_____   _____bath   _____gum

3. false_____   brother_____   _____winked

4. _____man   wheel_____   rocking_____

5. god_____   _____Time   _____hood

6. _____nail   fore_____   _____tip

7. gun_____   gold_____   black_____

8. flying_____   _____bag   oriental_____   _____sweeper

9. _____cutter   sugar_____   _____jar   _____crumb

10. _____gazer   movie_____   _____burst   shooting_____

11. in_____   _____burn   _____step   _____street

12. _____crab   _____pin   _____size   _____fish

13. _____plug   camp_____   forest_____   _____bird

14. back_____   _____tight   _____proof   salt_____

15. _____pot   _____corn   ground_____   green_____

Language Skills:
What Comes Before or After?

Complete the familiar expressions, phrases, or compounds by adding the same word to each blank in the set. Look at the following example before you begin.

EXAMPLE: Pac_____   _____kind   Spider_____
Answer: man

1. hard_____   _____apple   _____cane

2. fire_____   _____set   crush_____

3. business_____   _____perfect   capital_____

4. _____sticks   weak_____   _____tank

5. thin_____   _____cream   _____skates

6. _____West   _____board   piano_____

7. _____angle   _____away   _____hand

8. _____office   hitching_____   goal_____   _____age

9. _____sign   short_____   _____gap   whistle_____

10. _____puff   baby_____   _____keg   _____blue

11. saw_____   wooden_____   _____race   _____shoe

12. dinner_____   _____glass   silver_____   gold_____

13. _____pudding   stale_____   _____stuffing   _____crumbs

14. trade_____   hall_____   _____Twain   test_____

15. hot_____   _____put   _____gun   long_____

ANSWERS TO LANGUAGE SKILLS SECTION (Some answers may vary. Use your discretion.)

LS-1

1. ice	4. life	7. flat	10. land	13. saw
2. heart	5. dog	8. quarter	11. news	14. ship
3. back	6. draw	9. fore	12. road	15. hard

LS-2

1. bed	4. sea	7. paper	10. rain	13. grand
2. hand	5. hand	8. foot	11. blue	14. snow
3. love	6. play	9. house	12. pass	15. cross

LS-3

1. prime	4. Swiss	7. cross	10. head	13. picture
2. soft	5. black	8. red	11. window	14. wise
3. chicken	6. French	9. bird	12. China	15. egg

LS-4

1. salad	4. blue	7. mineral	10. Easter	13. light
2. electric	5. powder	8. blue	11. sand	14. watch
3. cold	6. salt	9. side	12. silk	15. crab

LS-5

1. shell	4. bag	7. light	10. case	13. berry
2. cast	5. fast	8. work	11. board	14. side
3. less	6. storm	9. ship	12. back	15. beam

LS-6

1. cake	4. fruit	7. stick	10. wave	13. point
2. way	5. leaf	8. board	11. box	14. house
3. nail	6. glass	9. top	12. paper	15. tree

LS-7

1. bill	4. ware	7. stone	10. bar	13. eye
2. blue	5. mill	8. green	11. door	14. bean
3. paint	6. block	9. line	12. red	15. match

LS-8

1. black	4. some	7. milk	10. fly	13. leg
2. pea	5. wheel	8. cap	11. shell	14. hand
3. spoon	6. weed	9. bug	12. ball	15. book

LS-9

1. earth	4. house	7. goose	10. line	13. fruit
2. pop	5. some	8. side	11. storm	14. well
3. pot	6. water	9. door	12. pea	15. net

LS-10

1. over	4. place	7. tennis	10. stick	13. tea
2. saw	5. suit	8. yard	11. ever	14. break
3. black	6. class	9. ball	12. house	15. work

LS-11

1. sweep	4. chair	7. smith	10. star	13. fire
2. bubble	5. father	8. carpet	11. side	14. water
3. hood	6. finger	9. cookie	12. king	15. pepper

LS-12

1. candy	4. fish	7. right	10. powder	13. bread
2. proof	5. ice	8. post	11. horse	14. mark
3. letter	6. key	9. stop	12. plate	15. shot

Section III
Categorizing

Suggested Time: 15 minutes
(2 minutes for directions, 13 minutes for skill activity)

There are two types of categorizing activities in this section. In some of the activities students must supply missing answers in a grid. Special rules for scoring the grid activities are explained on those pages. The other activities challenge students to classify lists of words. These activities are scored according to the **number of different categories** created. Students must include at least two items in each category. When time is up, total the points on each team member's activity page. Each correct answer is awarded one point. Tally each team's total and record it on the Scoresheet next to the team's name.

C-1
Categorizing
Help Wanted!

On this page you will find a list of occupations. Categorize the occupations by placing them in groups. Try to think of unusual groupings and give each group a title. An example is started for you. You may use the same occupation in more than one category!

carpet layer	doctor	cook	airline pilot
oceanographer	barber	writer	dentist
teacher	bank teller	nurse	T.V. newscaster
truck driver	carpenter	gardener	veterinarian
fishing-boat captain	artist	accountant	photographer

TRAVEL
airline pilot

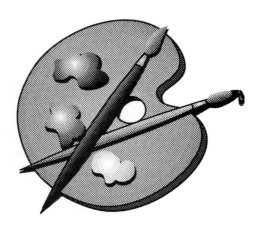

Categorizing
Be a Good Sport!

On this page you will find a list of popular sports and games. Categorize these activities by placing them in groups. Try to think of unusual groupings and give each group a title. An example is started for you. You may use the same sport or game in more than one category!

baseball	skiing	soccer	bowling
tennis	horseshoes	basketball	surfing
darts	football	fishing	ice skating
swimming	hockey	jump rope	roller blading
ping-pong	boxing	track	golf

SUMMER SPORTS
    golf

Categorizing
Creative People

In this activity you are to fill in the grid with words that begin with the letters on the left. These words must fit into the categories listed above the grid. Try to think of more than one word for each category. Compare your completed grid with those of your classmates. Score two points for words that no one else recorded. Score one point if more than one person thought of the same word. The time limit is thirteen minutes from the time you are told to begin. A few examples have been filled in for you.

	INVENTORS	ARTISTS	COMPOSERS	WRITERS
C				
R				
E	Edison			
A				Alcott
T				
E				
S		Seurat		

SCORE _____

NAME _____

Categorizing
Exploring America

On this page you will find the names of people, places, special events, and things that are part of America and its heritage. Categorize the names by placing them in groups. Try to think of unusual groupings and give each group a title. An example is started for you. You may use the same name in more than one category!

LANDMARKS
Statue of Liberty

Plymouth Rock
Benjamin Franklin
Thanksgiving
Declaration of Independence
Statue of Liberty
Susan B. Anthony
Boston Tea Party
Mesa Verde Park
Neil Armstrong
Pilgrims
Constitution
Martin Luther King, Jr.
Independence Hall
Labor Day
Painted Desert
John Glenn
Liberty Bell
John Kennedy
Appalachian Trail
Christopher Columbus
Mississippi River
George Washington

Categorizing
Miscellaneous Objects

On this page you will find a list of miscellaneous items. Categorize these objects by placing them in groups. Try to think of unusual groupings and give each group a title. An example is started for you. You may use the same item in more than one category!

pencil	tennis ball	lemon	hammer
comb	nails	notebook	can opener
plum	lunchbox	paper plate	ribbon
napkins	wrench	chair	glass
candy bar	clock	trumpet	baseball bat

**THINGS USED
IN SCHOOL**
   pencil

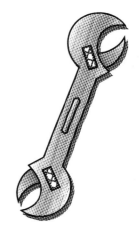

Categorizing
Let's Eat!

On this page you will find a list of many kinds of food. Some are more popular in other parts of the world. Read the list carefully and categorize the foods by placing them in groups. Try to think of unusual groupings and give each group a title. An example is started for you. You may use the same food in more than one category!

hot dogs	tacos	ravioli	fish and chips
egg rolls	quiche	apple pie	bagels
curried lamb	chocolate cake	pizza	lasagne
hamburgers	chow mein	souffle	enchiladas
tuna salad	ice cream	meatballs	lobster

DESSERTS
ice cream

Categorizing
At the Library!

On this page you will find a list twenty book titles. Categorize these titles by placing them in groups. Try to think of unusual groupings and give each group a title. An example is started for you. You may use the same book in more than one category!

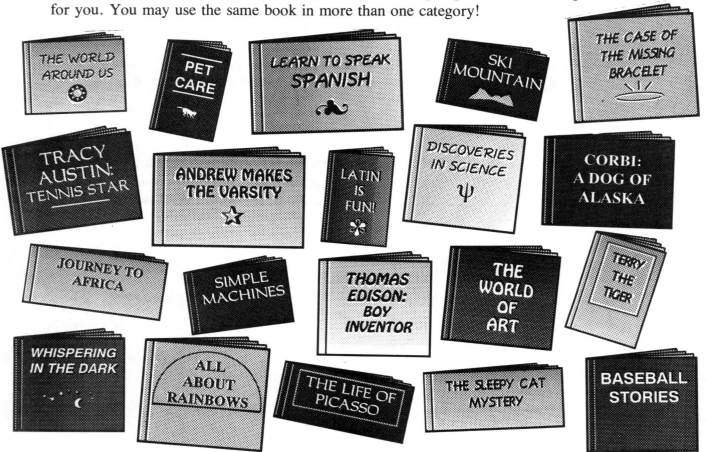

ANIMAL BOOKS
  Terry the Tiger

C-8
Categorizing
Figure Fun!

On this page you will find a variety of numbers. Your task is to categorize the numbers by placing them in groups. Try to think of unusual groupings and give each group a title. An example is started for you. You may use the same number in more than one category!

51	7	44	28
12	136	2	77
175	14	25	118
22	91	60	10
34	100	3	5

DIGITS
TOTAL TEN
136

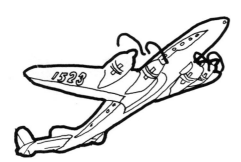

Categorizing
Transportation

On this page you will find a list of many types of transportation that are used throughout the world to enable people to move from one place to another. Categorize them by placing them in groups. Try to think of unusual groupings and give each group a title. An example is started for you. You may use the same form of transportation in more than one category!

train	submarine	taxi	automobile
rickshaw	helicopter	bus	ferry
houseboat	airplane	truck	elevator
sailboat	escalator	jeep	rocketship
tank	bicycle	go-cart	motorcycle
subway	kayak	monorail	Chinese junk

**USED BY
CHILDREN**
  bicycle

C-10
Categorizing
Happy Holidays!

In this activity you are to fill in the grid with words that begin with the letters on the left. These words must fit into the categories listed above the grid. Try to think of more than one word for each category. Compare your completed grid with those of your classmates. Score two points for words that no one else recorded. Score one point if more than one person thought of the same word. The time limit is thirteen minutes from the time you are told to begin. A few examples have been filled in for you.

	HOLIDAYS	HOLIDAY FOODS	HOLIDAY SYMBOLS
F			Fireworks
E			
S			
T		Turkey	
I			
V	Valentine's Day		
A			
L			

SCORE _____   NAME _____

Thinkathon I 47

C-11
Categorizing
Nature

In this activity you are to fill in the grid with words that begin with the letters on the left. These words must fit into the categories listed above the grid. Try to think of more than one word for each category. Compare your completed grid with those of your classmates. Score two points for words that no one else recorded. Score one point if more than one person thought of the same word. The time limit is thirteen minutes from the time you are told to begin. A few examples have been filled in for you.

	FLOWERS	TREES	LAND AND SEA ANIMALS	BIRDS AND INSECTS
E		Elm		
A				
R				Robin
T	Tulip			
H				

SCORE _____

NAME _____

C-12
Categorizing
In the Tool Box

On this page you will find a list of equipment and tools that are used by people in a variety of occupations. Categorize the tools by placing them in groups. Try to think of unusual groupings and give each group a title. An example is started for you. You may use the same item in more than one category!

ARTIST'S TOOLS
paintbrush

palette
crowbar
stethoscope
chalk
ladle
spade
golf club
paintbrush
scissors
hammer
paddle
measuring cup
baseball glove
screwdriver
wrench
pencil
broom
scalpel
baton
protractor
shears
microscope

Section IV
Brainstorming

Suggested Time: 15 minutes
(2 minutes for directions, 13 minutes for skill activity)

The activities in this section challenge students to generate a list of ideas or words within a given category. Encourage them to think of unusual responses. When time is up, total the points on each team member's activity page. Each correct answer is awarded one point. Tally each team's total and record it on the Scoresheet next to the team's name.

B-1
Brainstorming
Hats Off!

Special hats are worn by people in a variety of occupations as a part of their uniform or to protect them from environmental conditions. People also wear hats to enhance their appearance. How many different types of hats can you name? Try to think of some unusual examples. Have fun!

Brainstorming
Fun with Words!

Stretch your imagnation and try to think of as many words as you can for each category. Each word must consist of three or more letters. Have fun!

WORDS That Start with S and End with E	WORDS That Start with L and End with T	WORDS That Start with M and End with N

B-3
Brainstorming
What Lives in the Water?

Many things live in water. Try to list as many as you can. Remember, not only animals live in water! Have fun!

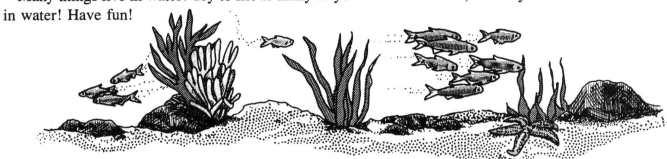

B-4
Brainstorming
Go Underground

List as many things as you can that are found underground. Stretch your imagination and have fun!

Brainstorming
All Kinds of Ships

In this brainstorming activity you are to think of as many different kinds of ships as you can. Stretch your mind to think of some unusual possibilities. For example, there are rocketships and there is friendship! Have fun!

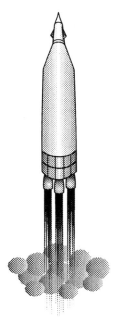

Brainstorming
Making Music

Since the earliest days of civilization music has been an important cultural activity. Stretch your mind to think of as many different ways of making music as you can. Try to think of some unusual possibilities! Have fun!

B-7
Brainstorming
World Landmarks

A landmark may be a famous building, a structure, a monument, or a geographical feature that has special significance to the nation or area in which it is located. For example, the Statue of Liberty is a landmark of America. See how many different landmarks you can recall. Write the location next to each. Have fun!

B-8
Brainstorming
Electricity

There are many things in your daily life that use electricity for power. Try to think of all the things in your home, school, classroom, and other locations that use electricity. Have fun!

Brainstorming
An Empty Can

Each day many empty cans are thrown away. Try to think of as many uses as you can for an empty can. Have fun!

Brainstorming
Let's Communicate!

People communicate with each other in many different ways. Stretch your imagination to include unusual possibilities that no one else will think of!

B-11
Brainstorming
Up in the Air

Stretch your imagination and think of many different things that move through the air. Try to think of some unusual answers. Have fun!

B-12
Brainstorming
Uses for a Pencil

Of course, pencils are used for writing and drawing. How else might you use a pencil? Stretch your imagination and try to think of some creative ideas! Have fun!

Section V
Memory Skills

Suggested Time: 15 minutes
(2 minutes for directions, 13 minutes for skill activity)

This section contains a variety of memory-skill activities. Each activity page contains pictured items, word lists, or word and picture combinations. Elicit from the students that it sometimes helps to try a memory trick, such as learning them in alphabetical order. Allow students two minutes to silently study the items on the page. Tell them when the two minutes are up and instruct them to turn over the page. They will have eleven additional minutes to record their answers in word and/or picture. When time is up, total the points on each team member's activity page. Each correct answer is awarded one point. Tally each team's total and record it on the Scoresheet next to the team's name.

Memory Skills
Sky Watch

On this page you will find words and pictures that are associated with the sky in some way. Study them carefully for two minutes. Then turn over the paper and see how many words and pictures you can remember. Good luck!

HELICOPTER

PLANET

THUNDER

ROCKETSHIP

VENUS

MARS

ASTEROID

RAINBOW

MILKY WAY

SOLAR SYSTEM

ASTRONOMY

METEORITE

Memory Skills
Math Terms

On this page you will find words, symbols, and figures that are associated with the study of mathematics. Study them carefully for two minutes. Then turn over the paper and see how many words, symbols, and figures you can remember. Good luck!

five	decimals
$+$	geometry
fraction	782
$-$	subtraction
66	46 x 2
▢	algebra
$4.59	sum
33⅓ %	octagon
hexagon	one hundred
division	▭

M-3
Memory Skills
Amazing Animals

On this page you will find the names of animals. Study them carefully for two minutes. Then turn over the paper and see how many of the animal names you can remember. Good luck!

frog	turtle
cat	alligator
kangaroo	horse
penguin	nightingale
dog	giraffe
lion	elephant
bear	opossum
mouse	sparrow
quail	jaguar
cow	iguana

Memory Skills
A Sign of the Times

On this page you will find twenty signs. Many are signs that you see every day in your daily life. Study them carefully for two minutes. Then turn over the paper and see how many of the signs you can remember. Good luck!

Memory Skills
DZQHIBT!

Can you remember the silly nonsense words and pictures on this page? Study them carefully for two minutes. (Hint: Do any of these nonsense words remind you of real words?) Then turn over the paper and see how many words and pictures you can remember. Good luck!

WNDO	FRYNPN	NBRHD
BSBL	LPHNT	SPRMRKT
LWNMR	PNCL	CMPTR
RFRGRTR	NTBK	PLGRND
CHMNZ	RHNCRS	WTRMLN

Memory Skills
The World of Wheels

On this page you will find the names and pictures of items that use wheels. Study them carefully for two minutes. Then turn over the paper and see how many words and pictures you can remember. Good luck!

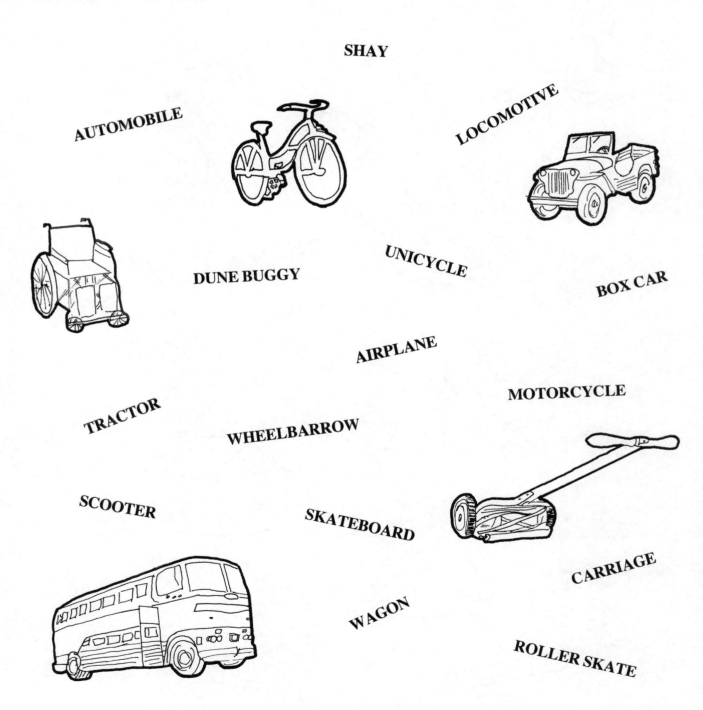

SHAY

AUTOMOBILE

LOCOMOTIVE

UNICYCLE

DUNE BUGGY

BOX CAR

AIRPLANE

MOTORCYCLE

TRACTOR

WHEELBARROW

SCOOTER

SKATEBOARD

CARRIAGE

WAGON

ROLLER SKATE

Memory Skills
Unrelated Objects

On this page you will find pictures of twenty objects. Study them carefully for two minutes.
Then turn over the paper and see how many pictures you can remember. Good luck!

Memory Skills
Around the House

On this page you will find pictures of objects that are commonly found in a home. Study them carefully for two minutes. Then turn over the paper and see how many pictures you can remember. Good luck!

Thinkathon I

Memory Skills
School Days

On this page you will find words that are associated with school in some way. Study them carefully for two minutes. Then turn over the paper and see how many words you can remember. Good luck!

pencil	notebook
book	blackboard
desk	globe
eraser	playground
teacher	bulletin board
school bus	lunch box
lunchroom	office
library	pen
report card	pupil
principal	fire drill

Memory Skills
Unrelated Objects

On this page you will find pictures of twenty unrelated objects. Study them carefully for two minutes. Then turn over the paper and see how many pictures you can remember. Good luck!

Memory Skills
Unrelated Objects

On this page you will find pictures of twenty unrelated objects. Study them carefully for two minutes. Then turn over the paper and see how many pictures you can remember. Good luck!

Memory Skills
Unrelated Objects

On this page you will find pictures of twenty unrelated objects. Study them carefully for two minutes. Then turn over the paper and see how many pictures you can remember. Good luck!

Section VI
I.Q. Testers

Suggested Time: 15 minutes
(2 minutes for directions, 13 minutes for skill activity)

In this section each competitive activity consists of twenty questions. Trivia questions, math and logic problems, language challenges, and decoding puzzles are included in each. Some clues to help solve the decoding puzzles are provided. When time is up, total the points on each team member's activity page. Each correct answer is awarded one point. Tally each team's total and record it on the Scoresheet next to the team's name.

I.Q. Testers

1. One word in the following group does not belong. Circle it.

   clarinet   trumpet   oboe   flute

2. Circle the misspelled word.

   musuem   murmur   mortgage   medicine

3. Fill in the blank so that the pattern is followed.

   3, 4, 6, 9, _____, 18

4. Use the following clue to name the mystery person: a famous Spanish artist known for his Cubist paintings.

   _____

5. The sport in which the following terms are used is _____.

   sweep   yardline   screen   sneak

6. Peter broke a 60-foot chain into four equal pieces. How many yards long was each piece?

   Each was _____ yards long.

7. The name of an animal is hidden in the following sentence. Circle it.

   The star attraction was the clown.

8. Which word most closely defines the first word? Circle it.

   repudiate: return   reject   repeat

9. Decode the following message. HINT: Be thrifty!

   C RGPPA UCXGF KU C RGPPA GCTPCF.

   _____

10. Whose face appears on the twenty-dollar bill?

   _____

11. One word in the following group does not belong. Circle it.

        clipper   houseboat   cutter   sloop

12. Find the misspelled word. Circle it.

        applause   appearence   apologize   apparatus

13. What comes next? Be sure to follow the pattern.

        4, 6, 12, 14, 28, _____

14. Use the following clue to name the mystery person: a famous pioneer who blazed the Wilderness Road.

        _____

15. Fill in the blank.

In 1922 Howard Carter discovered the treasures of _____'s tomb.

16. What number when doubled is two less than 50?

        _____

17. The name of an animal is hidden in the following sentence. Circle it.

        Place the blanket upon your bed.

18. Which word most closely defines the first word? Circle it.

        notorious: powerful   famous   expert

19. Decode this message. HINT: Be cautious!

        16-19-19-15   6-9-10-19-11-9   3-19-25   16-9-5-20!

_____

20. Ghost, stone, horse, and bristly are all names given to types of a small, hard-shelled marine animal. Name it.

        _____

I.Q. Testers

1. One word in the following group does not belong. Circle it.

    flamingo   gull   heron   lark

2. Circle the misspelled word.

    calendar   elementery   presence   skeleton

3. Fill in the blank so that the pattern is followed.

    1, 1, 2, 6, _____, 120

4. Use the following clue to name the mystery person: this poet who often painted word pictures of New England landscapes won the Pulitzer Prize.

    _____

5. In which city would you find Independence National Park?

    _____

6. If you multiply the number of eggs in a dozen by the number of inches in two feet, what will your answer be?

    _____

7. The name of an animal is hidden in the following sentence. Circle it.

    Please allow more travel time in bad weather.

8. Which word most closely defines the first word? Circle it.

    implicate: irritate   involve   inspire

9. Decode the following message. HINT: Be tidy.

    5   18-9-1   6-22-19-19-17   23-1-9-9-20-23   7-16-9-5-18

    _____

10. Name the Virginia estate that was the home of the first President of the United States.

    _____

11. One word in the following group does not belong. Circle it.

        Pennsylvania   Virginia   Massachusetts   Tennessee

12. Find the misspelled word. Circle it.

        surround   suprise   vacuum   temporary

13. Fill in the blank so that the pattern is followed.

        40, 39, 37, _____, 30

14. Use the following clue to name the mystery person: this author of *Poor Richard's Almanac* served his new nation as an inventor, statesman, and civic leader.

      _____

15. Name the popular English sport that is played with a wicket and ball and has an 11-person team.

      _____

16. How many times must you walk around a playground that is 325 feet long and 203 feet wide in order to walk a mile?

      _____

17. The name of a country is hidden in the following sentence. Circle it.

      They purchased flowers at the Garden Market.

18. Which word most closely defines the first word? Circle it.

      ferocious: fierce   firm   rude

19. Decode this message. HINT: What's cooking?

      XSS QERC GSSOW WTSMP XLI FVSXL.

_____

20. Name the famous author whose real name was Samuel Langhorne Clemens.

      _____

I.Q. Testers

1. One word in the following group does not belong. Circle it.

    Peru   Cuba   Mexico   Brazil

2. Circle the misspelled word.

    government   familiar   similiar   prevail

3. What comes next? Be sure to follow the pattern.

    2, 7, 17, 32, _____

4. Use the following clue to name the mystery person: winner of four gold medals in track and field at the 1936 Olympic games.

    _____

5. Found mostly in tropical seas, this limestone formation is made from the bodies of tiny animals. Name it!

    _____

6. If you lived in California and called your friend in New Jersey at 8:00 P.M. California time, what time would it be in New Jersey?

    It would be _____.

7. The name of an animal is hidden in the following sentence. Circle it.

    Bob can do each task quickly.

8. Which word most closely defines the first word? Circle it.

    counterfeit: fake   ridiculous   imaginary

9. Decode the following message. HINT: Be careful!

    8-11-26-26-11-24   25-7-12-11   26-14-7-20   25-21-24-24-5.

    _____

10. In Roman mythology he was the god of the sea. Name him.

    _____

11. One word in the following group does not belong. Circle it.

                            yard   rod   peck   fathom

12. Find the misspelled word. Circle it.

                    presence   operator   imagry   mannequin

13. What comes next? Be sure to follow the pattern.

                          106, 101, 91, 86, _____

14. Use the following clue to name the mystery person: an English scientist known for his theories on motion, optics, color, and gravity.

                        _____

15. The sport in which the following terms are used is _____.

                    set   love   ace   deuce

16. Find two numbers whose sum is 12 and whose product is less than twelve but not zero.

                        _____

17. The name of a country is hidden in the following sentence. Circle it.

                    Before I had lunch, I let out the dog.

18. Which word most closely defines the first word? Circle it.

                    disperse: combine   exclude   spread

19. Decode this message. HINT: It's about time.

                    PSHHSF ZOHS HVOB BSJSF.

20. Name the popular storybook by Hugh Lofting in which the following characters are found: Gub-Gub, Jip, and Dab-Dab.

                        _____

IQ-4
I.Q. Testers

1. One word in the following group does not belong. Circle it.

      Virginia   Vermont   Georgia   Alabama

2. Circle the misspelled word.

      consceince   sumac   poison   concise

3. What comes next? Be sure to follow the pattern.

      3, 8, 18, 38, _____

4. Use the following clue to name the mystery person: monarch of the British Empire during the American Revolutionary War.

      _____

5. In which state would you find Yosemite National Park?

      _____

6. A coat and matching hat together cost $100.00. The coat cost $90.00 more than the hat. What is the price of the hat alone?

      _____

7. The name of an animal is hidden in the following sentence. Circle it.

      The cake recipe calls for pecans, almonds, and walnuts.

8. Which word most closely defines the first word? Circle it.

      frustrate: defeat   abet   instigate

9. Decode the following "artistic" message. HINT: In this code "PICASSO" would be written "KRXZHHL."

      Z KRXGFIV RH DLIGS Z GSLFHZMW DLIWH.

_____

10. Which was the first state to ratify the U.S. Constitution?

      _____

11. One word in the following group does not belong. Circle it.

        onion   potato   carrot   pepper

12. Find the misspelled word. Circle it.

        restaurant   celophane   colonel   designate

13. What comes next? Be sure to follow the pattern.

$$2, 5, 9, 14, \underline{\hspace{2cm}}$$

14. Use the following clue to name the mystery person: this great baseball player was known as "The Sultan of Swat."

        _____

15. What do the letters in the acronym NASA represent?

        _____

16. A swimmer going downstream completes one half of a 3-mile race in a half an hour. It takes her twice as long to return. What is the average speed of the swimmer?

        _____

17. The name of an animal is hidden in the following sentence. Circle it.

        Billy jumped over the fence.

18. Which word most closely defines the first word? Circle it.

        ghastly: ruddy   grim   fresh

19. Decode this "seasonal" message. HINT: In this code, "GOLDEN" would be written "WEBTUD."

        YD JXU WEET EBT IKCCUHJYCU.

20. How many time zones are there in the continental United States? Can you name them?

        _____

_____

I.Q. Testers

1. One word in the following group does not belong. Circle it.

    rabbit   mouse   koala   hamster

2. Circle the misspelled word.

    erase   easily   antelope   racoon

3. Fill in the blank so that the pattern is followed.

    5, 3, 6, 4, _____, 5

4. Use the following clue to name the mystery person: when elected President of the United States in 1961, he was the youngest person ever elected to that office.

    _____

5. The word "cardiac" refers to which organ of the body?

    _____

6. The cost of everything in a certain grocery store is based upon the price of eggs. Eggs cost $1.00 per dozen. A loaf of bread cost the same as a dozen eggs. A can of coffee is triple the price. A box of tea is double the price. A package of cheese is one half the price. Suppose a shopper buys one dozen eggs, a loaf of bread, a can of coffee, a box of tea, and a package of cheese. What will the shopper spend for these items?

    _____

7. The name of an animal is hidden in the following sentence. Circle it.

    This is our family's favorite restaurant.

8. Which word most closely defines the first word? Circle it.

    leisure: business   vacation   toil

9. Decode the following message. HINT: In the garden.

    1   19-4-20-2   3-20   1   19-4-20-2   3-20   1   19-4-20-2.

    _____

10. Name the westernmost state capital of the United States.

    _____

11. One word in the following group does not belong. Circle it.

   banana   orange   lemon   grapefruit

12. Find the misspelled word. Circle it.

   feminine   sergeant   goverment   piece

13. What comes next? Be sure to follow the pattern.

   1, 3, 6, _____, 15

14. Use the following clue to name the mystery person: she helped on the battlefields during the Revolutionary War by bringing water to the men.

   _____

15. In what state will you find Mt. Rushmore?

   _____

16. A bag holding 36 marbles is divided evenly between two boys. Half of the marbles received by each boy are blue. What is the total number of blue marbles?

   _____

17. The name of an animal is hidden in the following sentence. Circle it.

   With a hop, a skip, and a jump, we played the game.

18. Which word most closely defines the first word? Circle it.

   important: irrelevant   pressing   unburdened

19. Decode this message. HINT: What's the password?

   ⌐⌐⌐⌐⌐⌐, ⌐⌐⌐⌐ ⌐⌐⌐⌐ ⌐⌐⌐⌐⌐ ?

20. What is the real (astrological) name of the Big Dipper?

   _____

I.Q. Testers

1. One word in the following group does not belong. Circle it.

     airplane   moped   wheelbarrow   motorcycle

2. Circle the misspelled word.

     aspen   maple   ceder   sequoia

3. What comes next? Be sure to follow the pattern.

     30, 25, 21, 18, _____

4. Use the following clue to name the mystery person: she helped finance the discovery of the "New World."

     _____

5. In what part of the body will you find vertebrae?

     _____

6. Place two plus signs and two minus signs in the following group of numerals so that you form a true number sentence.

     5 4 3 5 7 = 4

7. The name of a country is hidden in the following sentence. Circle it.

     Sue has pain in her infected finger.

8. Which word most closely defines the first word? Circle it.

     singular: musical   individual   apart

9. Decode the following message. HINT: A nursery rhyme. "ATE" would be "26-7-22."

     15-18-7-7-15-22   17-26-24-16   19-12-9-13-22-9

_____

10. What are the names of Donald Duck's nephews?

     _____, _____, and_____

11. One word in the following group does not belong. Circle it.

date   coconut   orange   strawberry

12. Find the misspelled word. Circle it.

mathematics   geography   langauge   science

13. What comes next? Be sure to follow the pattern.

A, D, H, M, _____

14. Use the following clue to name the mystery person: this real person is the owner of Winnie-the-Pooh and the son of the author of the book.

_____

15. Who was the first vice-president of the United States of America?

_____

16. Drew is soon to celebrate a birthday. He is now 58 months old. How old (in years) will he be on his next birthday?

_____

17. The name of a country is hidden in the following sentence. Circle it.

This globe measures 32 inches in diameter.

18. Which word most closely defines the first word? Circle it.

huge: big   gigantic   large

19. Decode this message. HINT: There are four A's in this weather message.

19-5-3-16,   19-5-3-16,   10-2   5-23-5-25.

20. What plant was used by the ancient Egyptians, Greeks, and Romans to make a material on which to write?

_____

ANSWERS TO I.Q. TESTERS SECTION

IQ-1

1. trumpet
2. musuem (museum)
3. 13
4. Picasso
5. football
6. 5 yards
7. rat
8. reject
9. A penny saved is a penny earned.
10. Andrew Jackson
11. houseboat
12. appearence (appearance)
13. 30
14. Daniel Boone
15. Tutankhamen (King Tut)
16. 24
17. pony
18. famous
19. Look before you leap!
20. crab

IQ-2

1. lark
2. elementery (elementary)
3. 24
4. Robert Frost
5. Philadelphia
6. 288
7. seal
8. involve
9. A new broom sweeps clean.
10. Mt. Vernon
11. Tennessee (not one of 13 original states)
12. suprise (surprise)
13. 34
14. Ben Franklin
15. cricket
16. 5 times
17. Denmark
18. fierce
19. Too many cooks spoil the broth.
20. Mark Twain

IQ-3

1. Brazil (speak Portuguese)
2. similiar (similar)
3. 52
4. Jesse Owens
5. coral
6. 11:00 P.M.
7. doe
8. fake
9. Better safe than sorry.
10. Neptune
11. peck
12. imagry (imagery)
13. 76
14. Sir Isaac Newton
15. tennis
16. 11 and 1
17. Chile
18. spread
19. Better late than never.
20. *Dr. Doolittle*

IQ-4

1. Vermont (north of Mason-Dixon Line)
2. consceince (conscience)
3. 78
4. King George III
5. California
6. $5.00
7. salmon
8. defeat
9. A picture is worth a thousand words.
10. Delaware
11. pepper (edible part grows above ground)
12. celophane (cellophane)
13. 20
14. Babe Ruth
15. National Aeronautics & Space Administration
16. 2 mph
17. dove
18. grim
19. In the good old summertime
20. Four: Eastern, Central, Mountain, Pacific

IQ-5

1. koala (not a rodent; a marsupial)
2. racoon (raccoon)
3. 7
4. John F. Kennedy
5. the heart
6. $7.50
7. ant
8. vacation
9. A rose is a rose is a rose.
10. Honolulu, Hawaii
11. banana (non-citrus)
12. goverment (government)
13. 10
14. Molly Pitcher
15. South Dakota
16. 18
17. panda
18. pressing
19. Halt, who goes there?
20. Ursa Major

IQ-6

1. wheelbarrow (no motor)
2. ceder (cedar)
3. 16
4. Queen Isabella of Spain
5. spinal column or back
6. $5 + 4 - 3 + 5 - 7 = 4$
7. Spain
8. individual
9. Little Jack Horner
10. Huey, Dewey, and Louie
11. strawberry (grows on a vine, not on a tree)
12. langauge (language)
13. S
14. Christopher Robin Milne
15. John Adams
16. five years old
17. India
18. gigantic
19. Rain, rain, go away.
20. papyrus

Scoresheet

TEAM: _____

SECTION	TOTAL POINTS SCORED
Section I: Analogies	_____
Section II: Language Skills	_____
Section III: Categorizing	_____
Section IV: Brainstorming	_____
Section V: Memory Skills	_____
Section VI: I.Q. Testers	_____

_____   **TOTAL TEAM SCORE**

This page should be duplicated for each team.

Certificate

This is to certify that

_____

has participated

in

THINKATHON

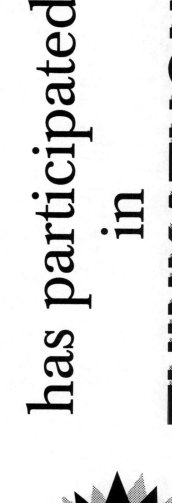
seal

Certificate Of Merit

This is to certify that

_____

was a member of the

Winning Team

THINKATHON

Seal